Nathan's Journey

"A Biographical Look Inside the World of Autism"

by Helen Barclay

Pictures by Ralph Beach

Graphics, Layout and Cover
by CF PrintGraphics

Marketing by
Alice McDougall at Marketing Incites

This book is dedicated to:

The kids at the YMCA
After School Program
in Melrose who asked,
"Why?..."

Nathan's classmates,
teachers, doctors,
his neighbor Mary,
and his grandparents

4/30/09

PREFACE
AUTISM INFORMATION FOR KIDS ONLY

(The following information is reprinted from a brochure published by the Autism Society of America.

Copies can be obtained by calling the Society at (800)3 **AUTISM**)

What is autism?

Autism is a development disability. Children with autism have a problem with part of their brain. That means, kids with autism develop skills differently than most other kids.

Children with autism may also have a different way of seeing, hearing, or feeling things. Like when you have gloves on in the winter and you try to pick up your pencil. It may be a little harder to pick up, but it feels different than if you didn't have gloves on.

Children with autism may have difficulty communicating. Some kids with autism cannot speak, so they may learn to use computers or a board with pictures on it to tell people what they want or how they feel.

People are born with autism and will have it all of their lives. But, they can learn and grow up to have jobs just like you.

Having autism is like living in a foreign country where you don't know the language or like trying to learn the rules of a very difficult game.

CHAPTER ONE
At Home

"Nathan! N-a-t-h-a-n!" Mom called out to her son. She knew her voice had reached his ears, but Nathan didn't respond. He kept running around and around the big fenced-in back yard while hissing and flapping his hands.

"Nathan, come to lunch!" Mom shouted while beckoning as she peered through the kitchen window. But Nathan flapped his hands and walked around in circles.

He muttered, "S-s-s-s...e-e-e-e...ph...ph...ph...pp." His voice got louder as he repeated the sounds.

Mrs. Barclay frowned and thought, I must call the school about Nathan's behavior and get him in to see the teachers early this week. Nathan is such a handsome little boy, she thought, but he doesn't talk and he does strange things. I think I will call his doctor and have him checked right after his birthday party next week.

When Nathan finally sat at the table, he began eating his crispy chicken with his fingers.

"Use your spoon, Nathan," Mom said quietly.

Nathan stared blankly at the spoon and kept pushing the chicken into his mouth with his fingers. He then pushed away his plate and stood by the kitchen window. He peered outside pointing to fleeting shadows. They were squirrels.

"Ah-ah-ah-ah," Nathan uttered as he looked around the backyard at the squirrels.

That night as Mom baked cookies for his birthday party, he moved back to the window, gazing at the stars in the sky. He pointed to the sky again.

I think he loves bright lights, Mom thought. She called out, "Nathan, move away from the window! It is very dark outside and anyone can see you." She was concerned because the kitchen lights outlined Nathan clearly in the window. None of the neighbors kept their outside lights on at night, and Mom always worried that someone would break into the house when Nathan pushed back the curtains to peer outside. Nathan stepped back from the window at the sharp sound of Mom's voice. He flapped his hands as he walked round the coffee table, making strange noises that ended in a high pitch.

"P-s-s-sss!.......phphphphphhhh!....nnnnnnmmmmmm!"

CHAPTER TWO
The Birthday Party

On Saturday morning Mom began setting the table for Nathan's third birthday party later that afternoon. Mom had invited lots of kids, some from the neighborhood, and others who were children of Mom's friends.

Just as she put the cake in the oven, Nathan screamed in frustration as he tried to put his shoes on.

"A-A-h-h-h-h!   ...E-e-e-e-e!" Nathan yelled.

Nathan had been practicing tying his shoelaces for over a month, but still needed help.   Mom rushed back to the living room where Nathan sat on the couch, struggling with his shoes. She helped him tie his shoelaces while explaining, "Nathan, be patient. You will learn to tie your shoelaces in time."

The smell of baked cookies drifted into the sitting room, and Mom walked quickly back to the kitchen, feeling comfortable that Nathan was finally dressed for his party.

When the doorbell rang, Dad opened the door.

"Hi. Through the hallway to the kitchen," he said as he greeted the parents and kids.

They streamed in one at a time, heading to the kitchen door.

"Hello, kids," Mom said when they reached the kitchen. She had worked very hard all day preparing the dining room and the front porch for the party. In the dining room, the cake, blue and yellow, sat in the center of the table. Overhead, Nathan's mother hung streamers with balloons attached at the corners. The kids were very excited and ran around the living room as they played with Nathan's toys. Nathan stood silently in a corner and stared at these "friends". He didn't join in the fun.

After everyone ate cake and ice cream, Mom called, "Come, everyone. Let's open the presents."

"Nathan, can we open your gifts?" Janet asked as she looked at Nathan.

Nathan did not answer, but his Mom said quickly, "Of course you can, Janet." Mom then turned to Linda, Janet's mother. She explained, "Nathan doesn't understand that these are his gifts. He doesn't even realize that this party is for his birthday." Then they both turned to the noisy activity in silence.

One guest eagerly tore off the wrapping paper. All the kids yelled, "What a beautiful car!"

Another child, Robert, said, "I love your baseball gloves, Nathan," as he put them on.

Nathan stood and smiled with his hands on his head. As the minutes passed, the yelling and screaming grew louder as each present emerged from its brightly colored wrapping paper.

Nathan covered his ears, overwhelmed by the noise. The kids kept shouting, and Nathan's Dad, sensing Nathan's discomfort, quickly stepped up and kneeled down.

"Let's wish Nathan a happy birthday, kids. Shall we sing?" he suggested.

Immediately the shouting stopped, and all kids held hands and circled Nathan singing, "Happy birthday to you, happy birthday to you, happy birthday dear Nathan, happy birthday to you."

Mrs. Brown, Dana's Mom, turned to Mrs. Barclay. "What is wrong with Nathan?" she asked in a puzzled tone.

"I don't know," Mom replied obviously concerned. "I plan to check with his doctor, Dr. Beech, and I'll call the school next week. Maybe he needs to be around other children. He's not talking yet and I'm really worried."

The parents continued looking on as Nathan struggled with the wrapping on one of his presents. He couldn't get his fingers to tear the paper off as quickly as the other kids. Nathan started throwing paper all over the floor and screaming. Startled, Bobby moved quickly away from Nathan.

Nathan's Mom said, "Sorry, Bobby. He is frustrated and angry."

That night, after everyone had left, Nathan's Mom said to his Dad, "I must call the Melrose school system about Nathan's behavior and find out about his starting school."

Dad replied, "I agree, dear, and don't forget to call Dr. Beech."

CHAPTER THREE
The Doctors

"The child may be deaf, Mrs. Barclay. Have his doctor check his hearing," the psychologist at the school told Nathan's Mom. Mom immediately called Dr. Beech's office for an appointment.

"Mrs. Barclay, he should see Dr. Fellows at Massachusetts Eye and Ear Clinic in Stoneham," said Dr. Beech's secretary. Then she made an appointment for Nathan to see the doctor.

Two weeks later, Mom, Dad, and Nathan arrived at the clinic.

"Come in, Mr. and Mrs. Barclay," Dr. Fellows greeted the family at the office door.

"We will test Nathan's hearing today," he continued calmly as he turned to Nathan. "Hi, Nathan, how are you today?" he asked with a smile then seated Nathan in a chair and put the headset on. Each piece covered Nathan's ears. "This won't hurt," Dr. Fellows explained calmly. Nathan stared blankly, then looked up at the teddy bear in one corner of the room.

"Mrs. Barclay, when I press the button, the teddy bear will tap the drums, and Nathan should hear the drums and the bells on teddy."

CLOONG. CLINNG. CLOOONG.

Nathan looked up quickly as the teddy bear's noises filled the room. Dr. Fellows pressed the buttons again and the teddy bear chimed up immediately. Nathan instantly turned his head.

"Let's go into my office," Dr. Fellows said, and he held Nathan's hand. Nathan's Mom and Dad followed quickly.

Dr. Fellows explained as he peered over his glasses at the family, "Nathan is not deaf. Why don't you take him to see Dr. Baker at Children's Hospital in Boston. He will have a lot more answers than I can offer about Nathan. I will talk to him after your visit. Good luck."

A few days later Nathan's Mom and Dad drove Nathan to the big hospital in Boston. Dr. Baker came out of his office and met them at the receptionist's desk.

"Hi, Nathan!" His words were cheerful. "Come in and sit down."

The friendly-looking doctor took Nathan's hand. Nathan walked along and looked back at his Mom and Dad as they entered the doctor's office.

Dr. Baker had a bag full of toys. He sat on the floor in his white coat over a dark blue suit and pulled out red, green, and blue blocks.

"Come here, Nathan. Let's play," he continued while looking at Nathan.

Attracted to the brightly colored blocks and the sound of Dr. Baker's voice, Nathan immediately sat beside him.

Dr. Baker put some blocks in spaces where they fit, then he gave some blocks to Nathan. Nathan twirled the blocks around and around, seeming to ignore everyone in the room including his Mom and Dad. The other doctors who had joined the group watched Nathan while he played. He didn't fit the blocks in their proper spaces.

After fifteen minutes of play, Dr. Baker looked up.

"Nathan may be autistic, but it is too early to tell. He is definitely developmentally delayed. He will need a lot of help. I think you should have the school give him special services or put him in a school for children with autism."

Dr. Baker also suggested to Nathan's Mom and Dad, "I will write a report for the school."

Nathan's Mom looked very sad, but his Dad said, "Don't worry. Nathan will be O.K."

CHAPTER FOUR
The Special School

Mom and Dad wasted no time finding a school for Nathan. They found a suitable school for autistic children in North Reading, a town twenty minutes away from where they lived. As they arrived, the principal, Mrs. Dodge, walked outside to greet them.

"Hello, Mr. and Mrs. Barclay. Come with me." She kneeled down as she spoke to Nathan.

"Hi, Nathan," she said and looked in his face. Nathan turned away avoiding her eyes.

She gently held his face and turned it towards hers. "How are you?" she said. Nathan was forced to look in her eyes, though he did not respond.

As they moved through the corridor, they saw several kids in a classroom through a one-way mirror. The children could not see them. They clapped their hands and hit themselves in the chest as they walked around in circles. Some kids banged their heads against the walls as they moved back and forth.

One boy lay on his back squealing, "Ech-ech eeh-eeh-eeh!" as the teacher tried to put a diaper on him. "This child is seven," Mrs. Dodge explained, "but he isn't potty trained yet. Most students in his class are still in diapers."

Nathan's Mom was horrified. "I potty trained Nathan last year!" she exclaimed. His Dad held her hand tightly and looked on. Mrs. Dodge responded, "That's great. He will go to Vida's class. The children in her class do very well. Many of them are talking and dress themselves without much help."

Nathan soon met Vida and his speech teacher. Her name was Alice. Vida's class sat around low round tables on stools. Every morning Vida had the kids sit on the carpets.

"Good morning, Nathan," she said. Holding Nathan's head, she forced him to look into her eyes.

Nathan pushed her hands away and yelled, "Mmmmmm-h-ah-ah!"

Every morning Vida sat on the floor and put her face to Nathan's so that he learned to look at her and notice her.

"I love you, Nathan. Good morning. How are you today?" Vida said as she cupped Nathan's face and stared into his eyes. He couldn't ignore Vida. Over time, he learned to love being with her rather than playing alone with toys in one corner of the classroom.

"Vida, Nathan love you," Nathan said one morning. Vida jumped up

and ran to the office while leaving the class with the teacher's aide. She called Nathan's Mom.

"Mrs. Barclay, I have good news. Nathan said 'Vida, Nathan love you', his first sentence!"

Nathan's Mom cried with joy. "I can't believe it. How great!"

From Vida's class, the children moved to music. "Feeling" words were used constantly in music class.

"When you're happy and you know it, clap your hands!" the kids sang every afternoon before leaving for home. Mom used to hear the sound of children's voices in tune as she walked down the corridor to Nathan's homeroom. Soon Nathan began singing along with the other children. When Vida gave him candy as a reward for joining in the sing-a-long, he said,

"Happy, Vida, happy, happy."

He seemed to understand what "feeling happy" meant.

One afternoon, he said to his Mom as he walked in the classroom, "Happy, Mummy, happy."

Mom immediately hugged Nathan. "Good talking, Nathan!" she responded in a pleased voice.

Twice a week Susan, the "Cheese Board" teacher as she was called at school, had sessions for Nathan. His Mom helped her set up for these classes.

"Nathan, you must walk on this board with holes. I'll help you, and you won't fall off," she reassured him. He tried to avoid the holes and listen to her tell him to perform tasks at each corner of the board.

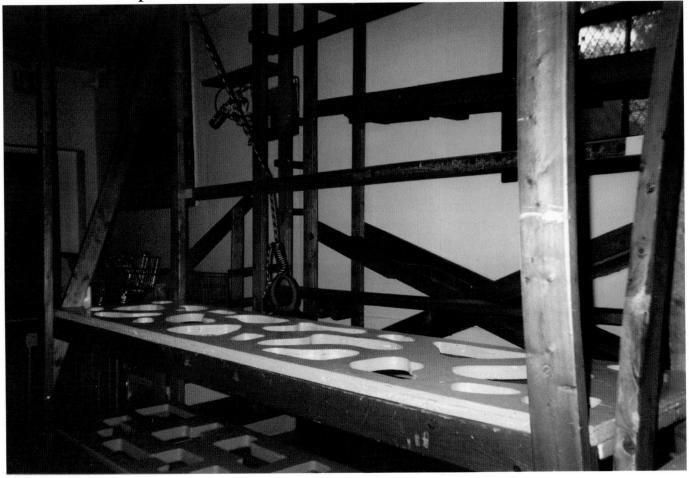

"Cut out the pictures, Nathan! Pour the water! Move quickly, Nathan!" Susan said firmly but quietly as Nathan struggled to balance on the high board and follow her directions.

Mom interrupted, "Will he fall, Susan?"

"No, Mrs. Barclay," Susan answered, while she focused on Nathan.

"Keeping him off the ground forces him to concentrate better on what he is doing."

"Oh?" Mom was puzzled, but she accepted the idea.

In the afternoons Nathan's speech teacher Alice showed him fruits made out of cardboard. These oranges and apples looked very real.

"Cut!" she shouted. Nathan then cut the fruits with a very sharp cardboard knife. It looked like a real knife. "He learns by seeing, then doing," Alice explained to Nathan's Mom as she observed the class that day.

Alice loved to shout action words, and Nathan loved to cut with his knife. WHOOSH. WHOOSH. All the cardboard apples flew into several pieces when Nathan forced the knife down.

"Apple, apple, apple," he repeated as he cut the fruits in small bits.

"Mrs. Barclay, Nathan cuts well. His motor skills are very good, better than most of the kids I think," Alice volunteered happily. She was very proud of how hard Nathan had worked that day.

"I can't believe how quickly the year went by," Vida said as she helped Mrs. Gray from physical therapy move tables onto the field for Sports Day.

"Yes, it sure has, Vida," Mrs. Gray replied. She placed each shiny trophy on one of the tables while talking to Vida.

On this cool sunny August morning the teachers enjoyed meeting parents at Sports Day. This day was also extra special for Nathan. He won all the races on that lovely clear Wednesday before school vacation.

When the races were over, the parents joined the students and teachers at the tables where the blue and silver trophies glistened brightly in the sunshine.

"Nathan, nice running. Here is your trophy for winning track and field. Congratulations!" Mrs. Dodge said and gave Nathan his long slender trophy. Then Vida placed a medal with a long blue and red ribbon around Nathan's neck. Nathan's Mom looked on proudly, capturing every moment with her camera.

"Mrs. Barclay, Nathan is making great progress," Mrs. Gray said. "We notice he excels at games and sports here. He is very good at basketball and baseball.

"I suggest you have him join the little league in his after school program when he returns to Melrose for school this fall. This is unusual, Mrs. Barclay. Nathan is fortunate."

She explained, "Most autistic students do not have such good motor skills. In fact they cannot play sports without falling!" Mrs. Gray nodded as she watched Nathan move quickly towards their kids on the playing field.

"I am very happy with his progress, thanks to Vida and Mrs. Dodge," Nathan's Mom replied. "I notice he loves to play with other kids," she added. "What a difference from two years ago when he had his third birthday party. I can't wait to plan his next party in September."

Mrs. Barclay smiled and explained, "Now he enjoys opening presents and playing with his new toys."

Then she took Nathan's hand and walked towards the car saying,

"Thank you for the great job you have done. His Dad and I are very proud of him."

"Bye, Nathan!" Vida called out to Nathan. Nathan waved back.

"Bye, Vida," he replied.

As Nathan and his Mom walked towards the car, the smell of freshly cut grass surrounded them. Some of Mrs. Barclay's worry dropped away and she smiled. Almost three years had passed and Nathan was ready to go back to school in Melrose just before his sixth birthday. As they walked through the parking lot, Mrs. Barclay remembered the first time she met Nathan's teachers at this special school. Then she thought, Vida and Alice have really worked very hard to help Nathan.

Soon they reached the white Honda. A little girl in a pink jacket walked by with her mother.

"Bye, Nathan," she said.

"Bye, A-n-g-e-l-a," Nathan replied squinting in the sunlight. Mrs. Barclay marveled at how much Nathan noticed other kids. She took a deep breath in relief, opened the car door and said, "Jump in, Nathan, and put your seat belt on."

Mrs. Barclay focused on the big black van in front of her as she drove Nathan home from his school for the last time. What a big improvement, she thought. I can't believe how much Nathan is talking. She smiled again while looking at Nathan through the rear view mirror.

Peering out of the window, Nathan saw a big yellow arch and pointed.

"McDonald's, Mummy," he said in an excited voice.

Speaking softly, Mrs. Barclay replied, "Yes, Nathan. That's McDonald's."

She started the car down route 28 towards Melrose and turned into the driveway with a sigh of relief as she heard Nathan's high voice call out from the back seat. "Home, Mummy, we're home."

CHAPTER FIVE
A New Adventure: Special Needs Class

A very tall woman walked into the special needs class on Nathan's first day at his new school. She was the homeroom teacher.

Nathan was flapping his hands while yelling, "We don't have time to do-o-o-it! It's cold outside."

Miss Vee wagged her finger at Nathan, "Sit down now, Nathan," she said in a firm voice. "Those are not your words. Use your own words."

Nathan sat down immediately. He started to cry. He had been crying all morning on the way to this new school. Mom comforted him as she put him on the bus.

"You will be fine, Nathan. It's your first day," she reassured Nathan. "Have a nice day, dear," she added as the driver closed the door and moved away.

In class, Nathan sat down. Then three minutes later, he jumped up.

"Ah-ah-ah," Nathan grunted and waved his paper.

"Sad news, Nathan. Sit down now!" Miss Vee said firmly trying to keep order in a class of very special kids.

This behavior continued for a few days. But with Miss Vee's help, Nathan learned to sit and concentrate in class.

When Nathan picked up the pencil, it fell out of his hand.

"Hold the pencil firmly, Nathan," Mrs. Bell, Nathan's aide, whispered with a sigh as Nathan struggled to stay on the line. Soon with her help, Nathan was able to draw many pictures for his Grandma and Grandpa who lived in the Berkshires.

Mr. Flood, Nathan's speech teacher, always had Nathan's scripts ready for speech class.

"O.K., Nathan, let's go through these sentences together," he said while he shuffled the papers around.

"The ball bounced down the stairs. The cat ran after the ball," Mr. Flood read aloud.

"Please say these words after me, Nathan."

Nathan repeated slowly, "The b-o-w-l b-o-u-n-ced down the st-a-i-rs."

Mr. Flood smiled brightly, "Very good, Nathan," he said and clapped his hands.

On a typical morning Miss Vee and Mr. Flood worked together to teach the class the days of the week and the months of the year. "Today is Monday!" Miss Vee exclaimed. "What day is it tomorrow, class?" she prompted next. "T-o-o-s-day!" the class chimed in.

"Good job, class." Miss Vee answered. She continued on with the weather. "Is it is raining outside, or is the sun shining? Nathan, look out the window and tell the class what you see outside." Nathan jumped up and ran to the window.

He replied, "It i-s ra-i-n-i-n-g...it i-s r-a-i-n-i-n-g." He dragged out the words as he repeated them slowly.

"Good job, Nathan. Say it only once," Miss Vee reminded Nathan.

The bell rang. It was twelve o'clock and time for lunch. Miss Vee told the class to line up for the cafeteria. The class left the room for lunch, but Miss Vee stayed in the room with Nathan. "Sit down," Miss Vee said as she picked up Nathan's tray filled with warm food. Nathan hated eating soft foods that were supposed to be good for him.

"Nathan, you must finish the mashed potatoes and green beans, or you won't get the corn chips," Miss Vee said sternly.

"O-o-e-w-a-a-h! N-o-o- p-o-t-a-t-o-e-s!" Nathan protested.

"Do not vomit, Nathan! We will sit here until you finish the hamburger, mashed potatoes, and green beans!"

Tears rolled down Nathan's face as he tried hard to swallow.

"No touching, please. Use your spoon," Miss Vee said in a determined voice. The children walked into the class as Nathan managed to swallow his last spoonful of beans.

"He's still eating," Bill whispered, and everyone giggled. Bill was the only kid who spoke clearly. He spent most days in the first grade but came to Miss Vee's speech class twice a week.

"To your chairs, class," Miss Vee said while she gave Nathan his chips.

Bill stopped talking, and the children sat quietly waiting for Nathan to finish his chips.

Nathan's Mom walked into the class to drop off his gloves and saw Nathan still eating in class.

"What's wrong, Miss Vee? Why is Nathan eating in class?"

"This is the best way we can control his tactile defensiveness," Miss Vee explained.

"Oh? I have never heard those words before. What do they mean?" Mom asked.

"It's a medical phrase we use to describe why some autistic kids, including Nathan, seem to dislike the feel of soft foods, Mrs. Barclay.

"I know you had mentioned how Nathan loved to eat cookies, chips, and crackers and wouldn't eat anything else," Miss Vee continued.

"I am so happy to hear you are working on this problem. I was worried about him touching and smelling the food before eating, then pushing his dinner away every night," Mrs. Barclay responded and handed Miss Vee the gloves.

"Don't worry, Mrs. Barclay. We will train him, and I am confident that he will change," Miss Vee assured Nathan's Mom.

Lunch break was over, and the kids sat down for the afternoon class.

CHAPTER SIX
The Family

Now that Nathan knew his birthday, many important holidays, and special days like Easter, Halloween, and Christmas, Mom and Dad wanted to make these days special for Nathan.

"This year we will get a big calendar and mark his birthday, Halloween, and Christmas in bright colors," Dad said.

"Excellent idea!" Mom added happily.

Nathan had fun dressing up for Halloween and going "trick-or-treating" in the neighborhood.

This year was the first time he understood it was Christmas Day. He gazed at the tree that Mom and Dad had

decorated. He couldn't wait for Mom to finish putting the turkey in the oven at 7 a.m. before he dived under the Christmas tree. He eagerly tore off the bright red and green paper wrapping on all the boxes displayed beautifully around the red tree stand.

After pulling the pretty paper off, he played with his favorite toys–a basketball and a shiny new car.

"Sssssshhhhh......ssshhh....sssshhh." Nathan's sounds filled the room as he ran the car along the living room carpet. Then like any other kid he yelled,

"Goin' to play basketball, Mummy!" as he ran out the back door despite the cold day.

Family time was special to Nathan. He learned to be very affectionate and now loved to hug and kiss Mom, Dad, and other family members and friends.

"M-m-m-mmmm." Nathan purred like a cat in a high pitched voice as he rubbed his head against his Mom's face,

....and cuddled up to his Dad.

He also loved to play games and make faces with his Aunt Cecile.

Many times Nathan begged his Mom and Dad to visit his grandparents in the Berkshires.

"I want to go to Gran'pa and Gran'ma's howse, Mummy," he pleaded. "When can we go?" he begged. "Tomorrow, we are goin' tomorrow, tomorrow?"

At his grandparents' house, Nathan liked to play games like 'peek-a-boo' with Grandma and Grandpa Barclay, or pose for photographs on their couch.

CHAPTER SEVEN
Spring In Jamaica

Nathan was very excited about visiting his Mom's family in Jamaica for the first time. Again Mom marked the big day in April on the calendar.

"We take a plane, Mummy?" Nathan asked. He was speaking so clearly now that Mom was surprised.

"Yes, Nathan, we're flying to Jamaica in April," she replied.

Nathan jumped up and down shouting "Jamaica!....Jamaica.!....Jamaica!"

His Jamaican relatives were surprised to hear that Nathan was autistic.

"There is nothing wrong with this beautiful child," Grandma Gordon insisted when she saw him.

No longer did Nathan scream when everyone talked at the same time. When friends and relatives dropped by Grandma Gordon's house to see him, Nathan ran around and around the coffee table. He squeezed by everyone's knees as they sat on the couch, determined to circle the oval table again and again.

"Nathan, sit down for pictures," his Mom said. He immediately stopped running and sat with the family. Nathan always enjoyed smiling for the camera. Mom took advantage of his love for the camera's flashing lights to get great photographs with his newly discovered Jamaican relatives.

"He gets excited around a lot of people, Aunt Gem, and he loves to be the center of attention," Mom explained to her aunt. Aunt Gem moved her long legs as she tried to avoid tripping Nathan when he ran by her.

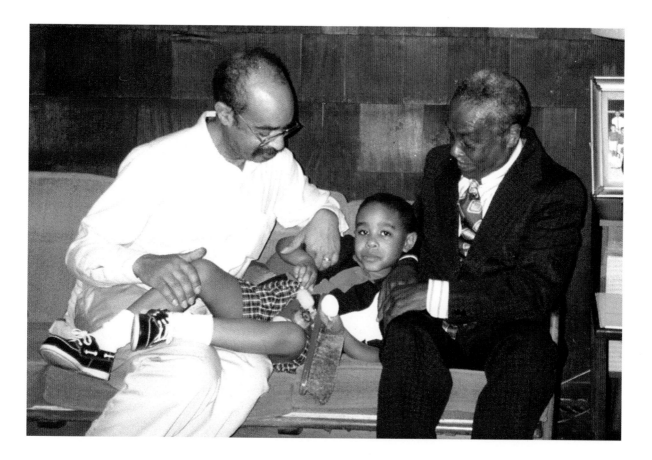

Mom snapped away while Nathan waited to go to the restaurant with Grandpa Gordon,

.......or as he stood with his Dad and his Uncle Bob while they talked.

Even when his aunts and uncles came to the house to visit, he would squeeze between them and smile for the camera.

Grandma Gordon visited him every year in Boston, but he had never seen her in her own home in Jamaica. She hugged him closely, and he jumped in front for another photo, happy to see his Grandma Gordon again!

"I love you, Aunt Ven!" Nathan said, waiting for Mom to press the button. "Smile, Nathan, or say 'cheese'," Mom spoke quietly as she focused the camera on the group sitting on the couch.

Nathan kept looking at Aunt Ven. "You are pr-e-t-t-e-ey," Nathan said to Aunt Ven between photographs.

Grandpa Gordon, a doctor, commented in a surprised voice,

"My Grandson is very friendly. I can't believe how much he loves the family. He behaves like many children I know."

After the photo sessions, Nathan got up and ran outside to play with the neighbor's dogs.

CHAPTER EIGHT
Inclusion

The large silver plane landed smoothly at Logan Airport at eight o'clock on a Sunday night. It was raining and cold for April. Nathan stared wide-eyed at the blue lights lining the dark runway. His Dad stood up, pulled a bag from the overhead compartment, then called,

"Come, Nathan. Let's go."

Nathan quickly followed between Dad and Mom. They moved towards the door at the front of the plane with the other passengers also waiting to get off. Nathan's vacation in Jamaica was over.

On Monday Nathan was back in school. A week later, Miss Vee called Nathan's Mom and Dad with the good news.

"Mrs. Barclay, Nathan has done so well in my class that I think he is

ready for our Inclusion Program," she said.

"Oh really, Miss Vee," Mom replied.

"Why do you think he's ready?" Dad asked.

"He writes clearly, knows the alphabet, and understands addition and subtraction problems, Mr. Barclay," Miss Vee added.

Nathan's Mom was excited. She responded, "Will he be able to keep up with the regular kids?"

Miss Vee replied, "We will have a special teacher for Nathan to provide him with extra help. She will assist him with any problems he might have in keeping up with first grade work. Her name is Mrs. Bell."

Nathan jumped up and down shouting,

"Mummy, Nathan's goin' to first grade! Mummy, Nathan's going to first grade! Nathan's going to first grade!"

Mom corrected Nathan as she usually did, "Say 'I', Nathan, say 'I'."

Nathan repeated correctly as he pulled on his socks, "I am goin' to first grade."

The little red van with the yellow school bus sign on the roof pulled in at 7:30 a.m.

"Byaheey!" Nathan yelled as he raced to the school bus.

Later, the bus driver moved close to the front of the school, and all the kids stepped out one by one. Mrs. Bell reached out her hand to Nathan, and he shook it.

"Nice job, Nathan," Mrs. Bell said in a surprised voice. As Nathan turned, his first grade teacher Mrs. Shaw greeted him,

"Hi, Nathan."

Nathan responded, "Hi, Mrs. Shaw. It's sunny outside. It's sunny outside. It's sunny outside."

Mrs. Shaw corrected Nathan quietly as some of the boys in the hallway giggled, "Only once, Nathan. Say it only once."

David, the small, fair-haired boy, whispered to his friend Tom, "He is strange."

"Quiet, David," Tom shot back. "Let's be good."

Although Nathan quickly passed through special needs class learning letters of the alphabet, spelling, writing, colors and shapes, he needed a lot of help in first grade. Mrs. Bell spent time patiently showing him how to work on math problems and read poetry without stumbling over words.

Nathan loved Mrs. Bell. She was very kind and pleasant with huge brown rimmed glasses. He worked very hard on reading and math just to please her.

At snack and lunchtime Nathan ate all his food just like the other kids. After all, he wanted to be just like the kids in first grade.

Soon it was time for recess. Tom said, "Let's shoot some baskets, guys." He looked at Nathan. "Want to join us, Nathan?" he asked.

"Y-e-e-s," Nathan replied in a deep voice as he smiled and moved his hands slowly across his face.

BUM. WHOOSH. BUM. WHOOSH. BUM. WHOOSH. The ball hit the backboard very hard and dropped into the net.

"Awesome, Nathan! Awesome!" a classmate, named Bill, shouted as Nathan moved rapidly towards the basket to score points. David was surprised, but not very happy. He was on the other team.

David looked at his partner Phil, "Get the ball in, Phil. You keep missing," he said in an urgent voice.

As the bell rang to return to class, Tom put his hand on Nathan's shoulder and said, "I will teach you to talk, Nathan, like us. Don't worry."

One day Mrs. Shaw told the class they had to choose a class president.

"That person has special jobs given to him or her like giving out calendars to other kids in the class," Mrs. Shaw explained to the class.

Lauren raised her hand, "How about Nathan?" she asked.

David interrupted her. "No, let's pick Jim," he said.

"O.K., class, write your names on paper and give them to me," Mrs. Shaw suggested.

When all the names were counted, Mrs. Shaw announced, " It's Nathan," and smiled. She was happy, though surprised, that most of the students had chosen Nathan for class president!

CHAPTER NINE
The After School Program

After class most kids went to the YMCA's After School Program in Melrose. Nathan also went with his aide, Jim.

"Mrs. Barclay, Nathan needs an aide to work with him because he may get excited, and we don't have enough teachers to help him stay calm," the program leader Mr. Bing explained to Nathan's Mom.

"The kids can get awfully noisy, Mrs. Barclay, and I know that Nathan

gets excited at the sound of a lot of loud voices."

Jim was chosen from many students who worked with special needs kids at the YMCA.

"Here is Jim. Kate, the administrator told me that you two talked on the phone but have never met," Mr. Bing said to Mrs. Barclay.

"Hello, Jim. Nice meeting you." Mom smiled and reached out her hand to Jim.

"Jim goes to the high school and has worked with the kids after school for two years. He is our best aide," Mr. Bing continued.

"Nice meeting you, Mrs. Barclay," Jim said and shook hands with Nathan's Mom.

After that first meeting, Nathan went to the YMCA after school every day with his aide Jim.

Nathan first started the program when he was four. That was three years ago. When the other kids wanted to play with him, Nathan wasn't interested in playing with them.

"How old is Nathan? Can he talk?" the kids asked Nathan's Mom.

She explained, "Nathan is four and he is autistic. He can talk a little, but not much. He loves to play basketball so why don't you ask him to play with you?" Mrs. Barclay added. "I am sure he would love to play."

The kids all chimed in a chorus, "O.K., Mrs. Barclay."

Now at seven, Nathan was back after spending time in special needs classes. The kids were very friendly. "Hi, Nathan, come and play with us," they greeted him as he walked in with Jim.

These kids loved to play games like kickball. On sunny days they played basketball and baseball outdoors.

Mr. Bing called the group together one September afternoon and said, "Kids, this year we will be playing in a basketball tournament against the Woburn YMCA. The games will start in two weeks."

The kids were very excited. They had practiced all year and were eager to play on the team. The coach Mr. Brown was choosing kids for positions that day.

"Who wants to play center?" Coach Brown called out. Most of the kids kept their hands up. Nathan wasn't sure what this meant, but he also raised his hand.

"He can't play center," David protested loudly. "He talks funny and we won't win, Coach," he added.

Coach Brown scratched his head as he hesitated, then said,

"O.K., let's see who does best in practice next week."

Tom walked up to Nathan as he left the gym. "Don't worry. We'll practice and I will teach you the words."

All week Nathan practiced shooting baskets at home in his back yard. "Goin' to play basketball outside,

Mummy!" he yelled as he raced out the back door. "O.K. Please remember to stay in the yard," Mom responded, then added, "And come in for lunch."

Back at the YMCA it was time to practice for the big game. Nathan got confused with the meaning of some of the words. Jim, at his side, whispered, "Throw, Nathan, throw! Jump, Nathan, jump!"

Nathan learned quickly to pass the ball and throw as the team yelled, "Nathan, throw the ball here!"

Sometimes he got over excited when the kids' voices grew louder, and he put his hands over his ears.

"Too many voices, too many voices," he repeated. Jim whispered again, "Stay calm, stay calm."

Immediately Nathan stopped flapping his hands and covering his ears. He got right back into the game.

"Nathan, it's your turn to take the ball," one of the boys on the team, John, called out. Nathan followed along and caught the ball.

On Tuesday Mr. Brown met with the kids to choose the team. He was very impressed with Nathan. As he watched the team practice, he noticed that Nathan never missed a shot. BUM. WHOOSH. BUM. WHOOSH. The ball hit the backboard and dropped into the net.

"You're great!" Coach Brown said in a surprised voice. Then he said to the team,

"Nathan is going to play center."

"I can't play with Nathan, Coach," David whispered as he watched Nathan lob the ball into the basketball net. Mr. Brown looked down at David.

"You will have to, David," he said, then added in a reassuring voice, "Don't worry. Nathan is good."

CHAPTER TEN
The Game

The Melrose team played well. They won the game 80 to 40.

"Good work, boys, and Nathan–great game!" the Coach added proudly as he looked at Nathan.

"Nathan, what do you say?" Jim prompted.

Nathan responded with a smile, "Thank you, Mr. Br-o-o-wn."

David walked over to Nathan, "I can't believe you scored 50 points! You're great!" he said in awe. "Give me five!"

They both smacked the palm of their hands together in the high five sign. Then David walked over to Nathan's Mom.

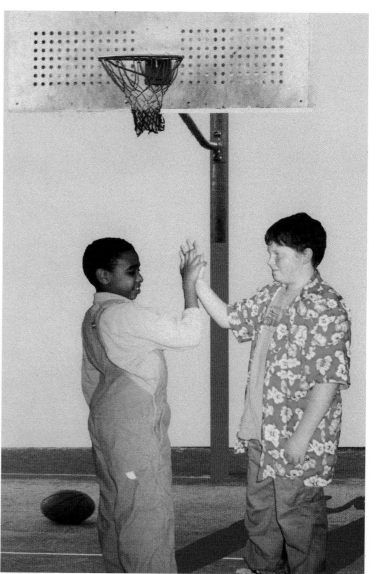

"Can Nathan come to my house next week, Mrs. Barclay?" he asked.

"We are going to play basketball at my party next Saturday, and I want Nathan to come."

Mrs. Barclay smiled proudly at Nathan, then she prompted him. "What do you say, Nathan?"

Nathan looked at David while clutching the team trophy and replied slowly, "Thank y-o-o,

53

David."

Mom corrected Nathan, "'You', Nathan, say 'you'."

Nathan repeated, "Thank you, David."

"We will be delighted to have Nathan over," David's Mom said. Turning to Mrs. Barclay she added, "I will send Nathan's invitation to school tomorrow."

Tom opened his eyes widely and shouted, "Whoopie!" Then he led his two friends towards the door with a hand on David's shoulder.

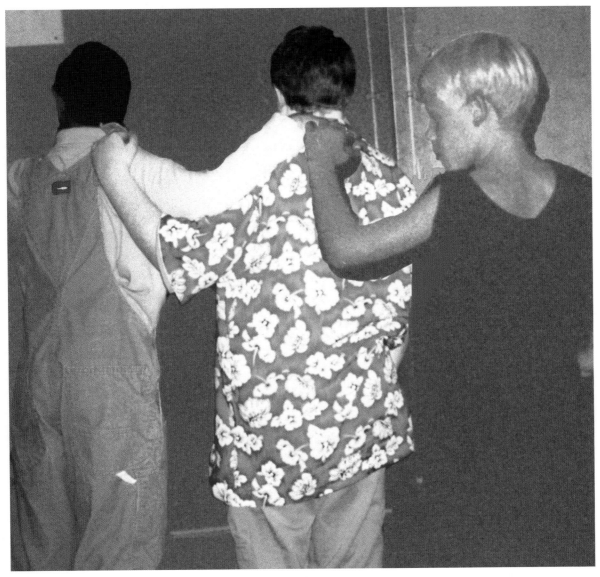

ABOUT THE AUTHOR

Helen Barclay is Nathan's mother. Since learning about Nathan's diagnosis, she has been a strong advocate for services for Nathan and all children with autism. She also supports organizations involved with raising funds for autism research.

CONTRIBUTORS

Ralph Beach is a well known artist and illustrator from the Boston area.

CF PrintGraphics has been in the business of providing printing and graphic services to the public for almost ten years.

ACKNOWLEDGEMENTS

**Thanks to the following individuals
who helped make this book possible:**

Mr. Doug Babbit
Mr. John Brady
Ms. Viktoria Brown
Dr. Donna Gilton
Ms. Cecile Gordon
Mrs. Doris Gordon
Ms. Primma-Latise Murry
Ms. Margaret Redfern
Ms. Oyinade Aderidigbe
Dr. Judy Zorfass
Nathan's therapists
Kathy Finklestein at
Broadway Business Services
and
CF PrintGraphics
Melrose, Massachusetts

Special thanks to the St. Paul AME Church,
Reverend Leroy Attles, Pastor
and The Angels Without Wings Choir

*A portion of the proceeds of this book
will be donated to Autism Research*